Reset Your Mind

30 DAY
CHALLENGE
DEVOTIONAL PLANNER

BY

RENEE HUFFMAN

30 DAY CHALLENGE-DEVOTIONAL PLANNER

BY

RENEE HUFFMAN

Published by iCHAMPION Publishing
P.O. Box 2352 Frisco, TX 75034
Content Edit by Nikia Hammonds-Blakely and iCHAMPION Publishing
Library of Congress Cataloging-in-Publication Data Publisher and Printing by iCHAMPION Publishing
Written By: Renee Huffman
Cover Design By: Renee Huffman
Illustrated By: iCHAMPION Publishing

ISBN: 978-1-7349212-9-8

CATEGORIES:
MIND & BODY
SELF HELP TECHNIQUES

I DEDICATE THIS BOOK TO

MY LORD & SAVIOR

JESUS CHRIST &

MY PRECIOUS MOTHER

BETTY ANN JACKSON

THIS DEVOTIONAL PLANNER BELONGS TO:

IF LOST, PLEASE RETURN TO:

EMERGENCY CONTACT:

Day 01

DATE

M T W T F S S

ROMANS 12:2

Do not conform to the pattern of this world but be transformed by the renewing of your mind. Then you will be able to test and approve what God's will is his good, pleasing, and perfect will.

Why is it important for you to reset your mind?

My Mind is
Being Renewed
Daily

DATE

I've got this

M T W T F S S

TODAY I'M GRATEFUL FOR

TODAY'S TOP 3 GOALS/PRIORITIES

1.

2.

3.

12 1 2 3 4 5 6 7 8 9 10 11

MUST BE DONE TODAY

1.

2.

3.

APPOINTMENTS/TIME BLOCKS

TO DO LIST

- [ ]
- [ ]
- [ ]
- [ ]
- [ ]
- [ ]
- [ ]

HEALTH & FITNESS

MEAL PREP

NOTES

PERSONAL NOTES

DO TOMORROW

1.

2.

3.

WATER INTAKE

Day 02

DATE

M T W T F S S

ROMANS 8:6

For to set the mind on the flesh is death, but to set the mind on the Spirit is life and peace.

Does your flesh control you or your spirit and how?

I Live a
Life of Self
Control!

DATE

I've got this

M T W T F S S

TODAY I'M GRATEFUL FOR

12 1 2 3 4 5 6 7 8 9 10 11

TODAY'S TOP 3 GOALS/PRIORITIES

1.

2.

3.

MUST BE DONE TODAY

1.

2.

3.

APPOINTMENTS/TIME BLOCKS

TO DO LIST

- [ ]
- [ ]
- [ ]
- [ ]
- [ ]
- [ ]
- [ ]

HEALTH & FITNESS

MEAL PREP

NOTES

PERSONAL NOTES

DO TOMORROW

1.

2.

3.

WATER INTAKE

Day 03

DATE

M T W T F S S

ROMANS 8:7

For the mind that is set on the flesh is hostile to God, for it does not submit to God's law; indeed, it cannot.(ESV)

How will you start to submit to God?

I am Fully
Submitted
to God

DATE

I've got this

M T W T F S S

TODAY I'M GRATEFUL FOR

TODAY'S TOP 3 GOALS/PRIORITIES

1.

2.

3.

12 1 2 3 4 5 6 7 8 9 10 11

MUST BE DONE TODAY

1.

2.

3.

APPOINTMENTS/TIME BLOCKS

TO DO LIST

- ☐
- ☐
- ☐
- ☐
- ☐
- ☐
- ☐

HEALTH & FITNESS

MEAL PREP

NOTES

PERSONAL NOTES

WATER INTAKE

DO TOMORROW

1.

2.

3.

Day 04

DATE	

M T W T F S S

JAMES 1:8

Such a person is double-minded and unstable in all they do.(ESV)

How can you stay singled minded for Christ?

My Mind Is
Focused
On Christ

DATE

I've got this

M T W T F S S

TODAY I'M GRATEFUL FOR

12 1 2 3 4 5 6 7 8 9 10 11

TODAY'S TOP 3 GOALS/PRIORITIES

1.

2.

3.

MUST BE DONE TODAY

1.

2.

3.

APPOINTMENTS/TIME BLOCKS

TO DO LIST

- [ ]
- [ ]
- [ ]
- [ ]
- [ ]
- [ ]
- [ ]

HEALTH & FITNESS

MEAL PREP

NOTES

PERSONAL NOTES

WATER INTAKE

DO TOMORROW

1.

2.

3.

Day 05

DATE	

M T W T F S S

ISAIAH 1:6

From the sole of the foot even unto the head there is no soundness in it; but wounds, and bruises, and putrifying sores: they have not been closed, neither bound up, neither mollified with ointment.

How will you regain soundness in your mind?

I am Healed
and I Have a
Sound Mind!

DATE

I've got this

M T W T F S S

TODAY I'M GRATEFUL FOR

TODAY'S TOP 3 GOALS/PRIORITIES

12 1 2 3 4 5 6 7 8 9 10 11

1.

2.

3.

MUST BE DONE TODAY

1.

2.

3.

APPOINTMENTS/TIME BLOCKS

TO DO LIST

- ☐
- ☐
- ☐
- ☐
- ☐
- ☐
- ☐

HEALTH & FITNESS

MEAL PREP

NOTES

PERSONAL NOTES

DO TOMORROW

1.

2.

3.

WATER INTAKE

Day 06

DATE

M T W T F S S

ISAIAH 26:3

Thou wilt keep him in perfect peace, whose mind is stayed on thee: because he trusteth in thee. (KJV)

What will happen when you keep your Mind on God?

I Have
Perfect
Peace!

DATE

I've got this

M T W T F S S

TODAY I'M GRATEFUL FOR

12 1 2 3 4 5 6 7 8 9 10 11

TODAY'S TOP 3 GOALS/PRIORITIES

1.

2.

3.

MUST BE DONE TODAY

1.

2.

3.

APPOINTMENTS/TIME BLOCKS

TO DO LIST

- ☐
- ☐
- ☐
- ☐
- ☐
- ☐
- ☐

HEALTH & FITNESS

MEAL PREP

NOTES

PERSONAL NOTES

DO TOMORROW

1.

2.

3.

WATER INTAKE

Day 07

DATE | M T W T F S S

2 TIMOTHY 1:7

For God hath not given us the spirit of fear; but of power, and of love, and of a sound mind. (KJV)

What are your fears? How do you plan to overcome them?

I am No
Longer a Slave
to Fear!

DATE | M T W T F S S

I've got this

TODAY I'M GRATEFUL FOR

TODAY'S TOP 3 GOALS/PRIORITIES

1.
2.
3.

MUST BE DONE TODAY

1.
2.
3.

APPOINTMENTS/TIME BLOCKS

TO DO LIST

- ☐
- ☐
- ☐
- ☐
- ☐
- ☐
- ☐

HEALTH & FITNESS

MEAL PREP

NOTES

PERSONAL NOTES

WATER INTAKE

DO TOMORROW

1.
2.
3.

Day 08

DATE

M T W T F S S

ISAIAH 43:18

Forget the former things; do not dwell on the past.

Write down things you need to forget.

I Will Let Go of My Past & Embrace My Future!

DATE | I've got this | M T W T F S S

TODAY I'M GRATEFUL FOR

12 1 2 3 4 5 6 7 8 9 10 11

TODAY'S TOP 3 GOALS/PRIORITIES

1.

2.

3.

MUST BE DONE TODAY

1.

2.

3.

APPOINTMENTS/TIME BLOCKS

TO DO LIST

- [ ]
- [ ]
- [ ]
- [ ]
- [ ]
- [ ]
- [ ]

HEALTH & FITNESS

MEAL PREP

NOTES

PERSONAL NOTES

DO TOMORROW

1.

2.

3.

WATER INTAKE

Day 09

DATE	

M T W T F S S

ISAIAH 43:19

Behold, I will do a new thing; now it shall spring forth; shall ye not know it? I will even make a way in the wilderness, and rivers in the desert. (KJV)

Write down God's vision for your life.

God Is Doing a
NEW Thing
In Me!

DATE | M T W T F S S

I've got this

TODAY I'M GRATEFUL FOR

TODAY'S TOP 3 GOALS/PRIORITIES

1.
2.
3.

12 1 2 3 4 5 6 7 8 9 10 11

MUST BE DONE TODAY

1.
2.
3.

APPOINTMENTS/TIME BLOCKS

TO DO LIST

- [ ]
- [ ]
- [ ]
- [ ]
- [ ]
- [ ]
- [ ]

HEALTH & FITNESS

MEAL PREP

NOTES

PERSONAL NOTES

WATER INTAKE

DO TOMORROW

1.
2.
3.

Day 10

DATE	

M T W T F S S

JEREMIAH 29:11

For I know the thoughts that I think toward you, saith the Lord, thoughts of peace, and not of evil, to give you an expected end. (KJV)

How will you walk in the peace of God?

God's Plans
Are to Prosper
Me, Not To
Harm Me!

DATE

I've got this

M T W T F S S

TODAY I'M GRATEFUL FOR

TODAY'S TOP 3 GOALS/PRIORITIES

12 1 2 3 4 5 6 7 8 9 10 11

1.

2.

3.

MUST BE DONE TODAY

1.

2.

3.

APPOINTMENTS/TIME BLOCKS

TO DO LIST

- [ ]
- [ ]
- [ ]
- [ ]
- [ ]
- [ ]
- [ ]

HEALTH & FITNESS

MEAL PREP

NOTES

PERSONAL NOTES

DO TOMORROW

1.

2.

3.

WATER INTAKE

Day 11

DATE	

M T W T F S S

NEHEMIAH 4:6

So built we the wall; and all the wall was joined together unto the half thereof: for the people had a mind to work.

How will you shift your mind to work for the Kingdom of God!

My Work will
Buid the
Kingdom
of God!

DATE	

I've got this

M	T	W	T	F	S	S

TODAY I'M GRATEFUL FOR

TODAY'S TOP 3 GOALS/PRIORITIES

1.
2.
3.

12 1 2 3 4 5 6 7 8 9 10 11

MUST BE DONE TODAY

1.
2.
3.

APPOINTMENTS/TIME BLOCKS

TO DO LIST

- ☐
- ☐
- ☐
- ☐
- ☐
- ☐
- ☐

HEALTH & FITNESS

MEAL PREP

NOTES

PERSONAL NOTES

DO TOMORROW

1.
2.
3.

WATER INTAKE

Day 12

DATE

M T W T F S S

JOSHUA 1:8

This book of the law shall not depart out of thy mouth; but thou shalt meditate therein day and night, that thou mayest observe to do according to all that is written therein: for then thou shalt make thy way prosperous, and then thou shalt have good success.(KJV)

How will you meditate on the word of God?

I Will Be
Propserous
And Have
Good Success!

DATE | M T W T F S S

I've got this

TODAY I'M GRATEFUL FOR

TODAY'S TOP 3 GOALS/PRIORITIES

12 1 2 3 4 5 6 7 8 9 10 11

1.

2.

3.

MUST BE DONE TODAY

1.

2.

3.

APPOINTMENTS/TIME BLOCKS

TO DO LIST

- [ ]
- [ ]
- [ ]
- [ ]
- [ ]
- [ ]
- [ ]

HEALTH & FITNESS

MEAL PREP

NOTES

PERSONAL NOTES

DO TOMORROW

1.

2.

3.

WATER INTAKE

Day 13

DATE

M T W T F S S

JOSHUA 1:9

Have not I commanded thee? Be strong and of a good courage; be not afraid, neither be thou dismayed: for the Lord thy God is with thee whithersoever thou goest.

What are you afraid of and how will you have overcome your fears?

GOD IS
With me!

DATE | I've got this | M T W T F S S

TODAY I'M GRATEFUL FOR

TODAY'S TOP 3 GOALS/PRIORITIES

1.

2.

3.

12 1 2 3 4 5 6 7 8 9 10 11

MUST BE DONE TODAY

1.

2.

3.

APPOINTMENTS/TIME BLOCKS

TO DO LIST

- [ ]
- [ ]
- [ ]
- [ ]
- [ ]
- [ ]
- [ ]

HEALTH & FITNESS

MEAL PREP

NOTES

PERSONAL NOTES

DO TOMORROW

1.

2.

3.

WATER INTAKE

Day 14

DATE	

M T W T F S S

PSALMS 19:14

May these words of my mouth and this meditation of my heart be pleasing in your sight, Lord, my Rock and my Redeemer.

What are you meditating on?

My Heart
Pleases The
Lord!

DATE | M T W T F S S

I've got this

TODAY I'M GRATEFUL FOR

TODAY'S TOP 3 GOALS/PRIORITIES

1.

2.

3.

12 1 2 3 4 5 6 7 8 9 10 11

MUST BE DONE TODAY

1.

2.

3.

APPOINTMENTS/TIME BLOCKS

TO DO LIST

- ☐
- ☐
- ☐
- ☐
- ☐
- ☐
- ☐

HEALTH & FITNESS

MEAL PREP

NOTES

PERSONAL NOTES

WATER INTAKE

DO TOMORROW

1.

2.

3.

Day 15

DATE	

M T W T F S S

PSALM 139: 23

Search me, O God, and know my heart: try me, and know my thoughts:

At what limit and depth are you willing to allow God to search you?

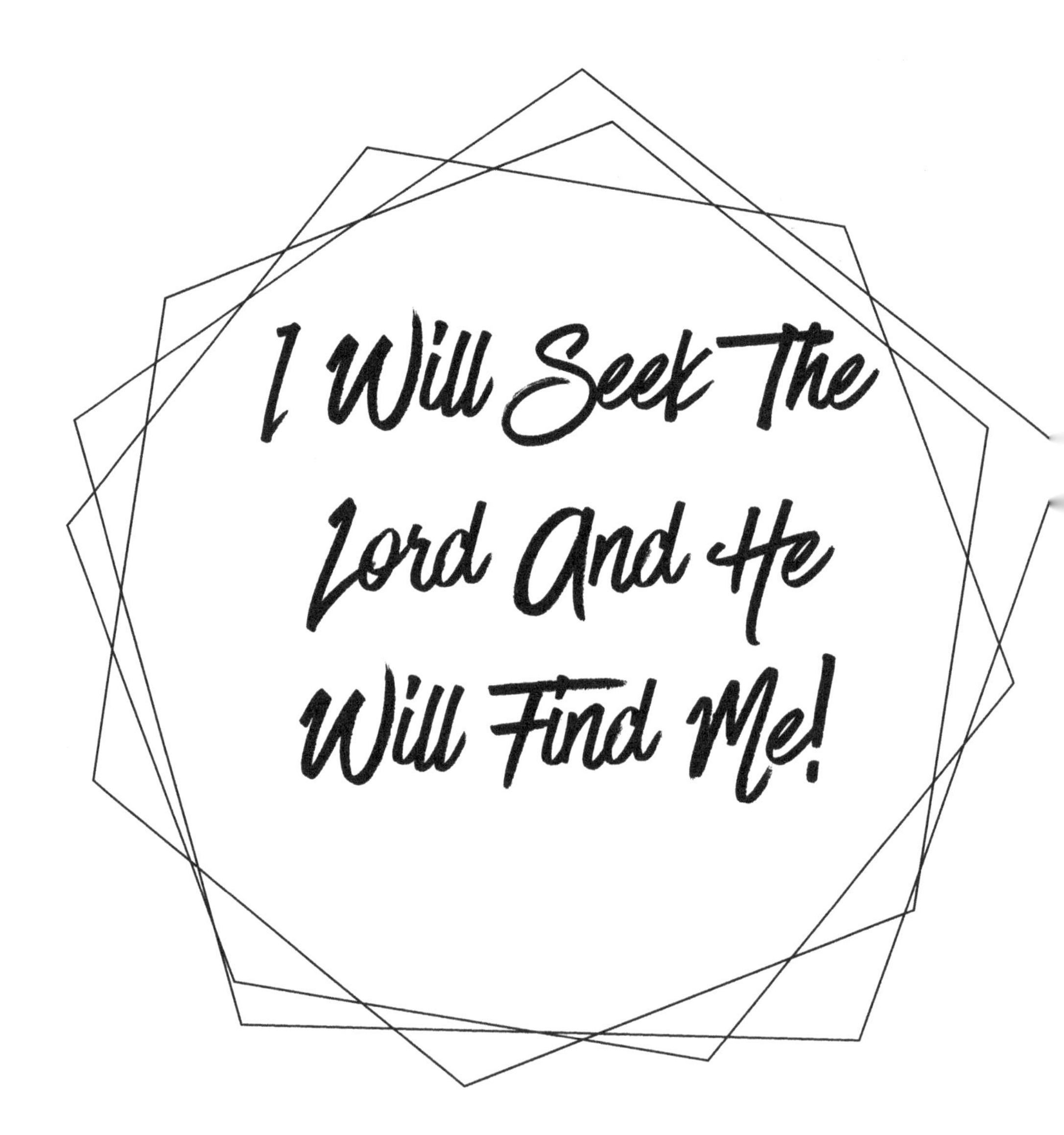
I Will Seek The
Lord And He
Will Find Me!

DATE

I've got this

M T W T F S S

TODAY I'M GRATEFUL FOR

TODAY'S TOP 3 GOALS/PRIORITIES

12 1 2 3 4 5 6 7 8 9 10 11

1.

2.

3.

MUST BE DONE TODAY

1.

2.

3.

APPOINTMENTS/TIME BLOCKS

TO DO LIST

- [ ]
- [ ]
- [ ]
- [ ]
- [ ]
- [ ]
- [ ]

HEALTH & FITNESS

MEAL PREP

NOTES

PERSONAL NOTES

DO TOMORROW

1.

2.

3.

WATER INTAKE

Day 16

DATE

M T W T F S S

PSALM 139: 24

And see if there be any wicked way in me, and lead me in the way everlasting.

How will you allow God to lead you?

God Leads
Me &
I Obey!

DATE

I've got this

M T W T F S S

TODAY I'M GRATEFUL FOR

12 1 2 3 4 5 6 7 8 9 10 11

TODAY'S TOP 3 GOALS/PRIORITIES

1.

2.

3.

MUST BE DONE TODAY

1.

2.

3.

APPOINTMENTS/TIME BLOCKS

TO DO LIST

- [ ]
- [ ]
- [ ]
- [ ]
- [ ]
- [ ]
- [ ]

HEALTH & FITNESS

MEAL PREP

NOTES

PERSONAL NOTES

WATER INTAKE

DO TOMORROW

1.

2.

3.

Day 17

DATE

M T W T F S S

PHILLIPIANS 4:6

Be careful for nothing; but in everything by prayer and supplication with thanksgiving let your requests be made known unto God.

What is your prayer request to God?

My Prayers
Are Heard &
Answered!

DATE

I've got this

M T W T F S S

TODAY I'M GRATEFUL FOR

TODAY'S TOP 3 GOALS/PRIORITIES

12 1 2 3 4 5 6 7 8 9 10 11

1.

2.

3.

MUST BE DONE TODAY

1.

2.

3.

APPOINTMENTS/TIME BLOCKS

TO DO LIST

- [ ]
- [ ]
- [ ]
- [ ]
- [ ]
- [ ]
- [ ]

HEALTH & FITNESS

MEAL PREP

NOTES

PERSONAL NOTES

DO TOMORROW

1.

2.

3.

WATER INTAKE

Day 18

DATE

M T W T F S S

PHILIPPIANS 4:7

And the peace of God, which passeth all understanding, shall keep your hearts and minds through Christ Jesus.

How will you walk in God's knowledge and wisdom?

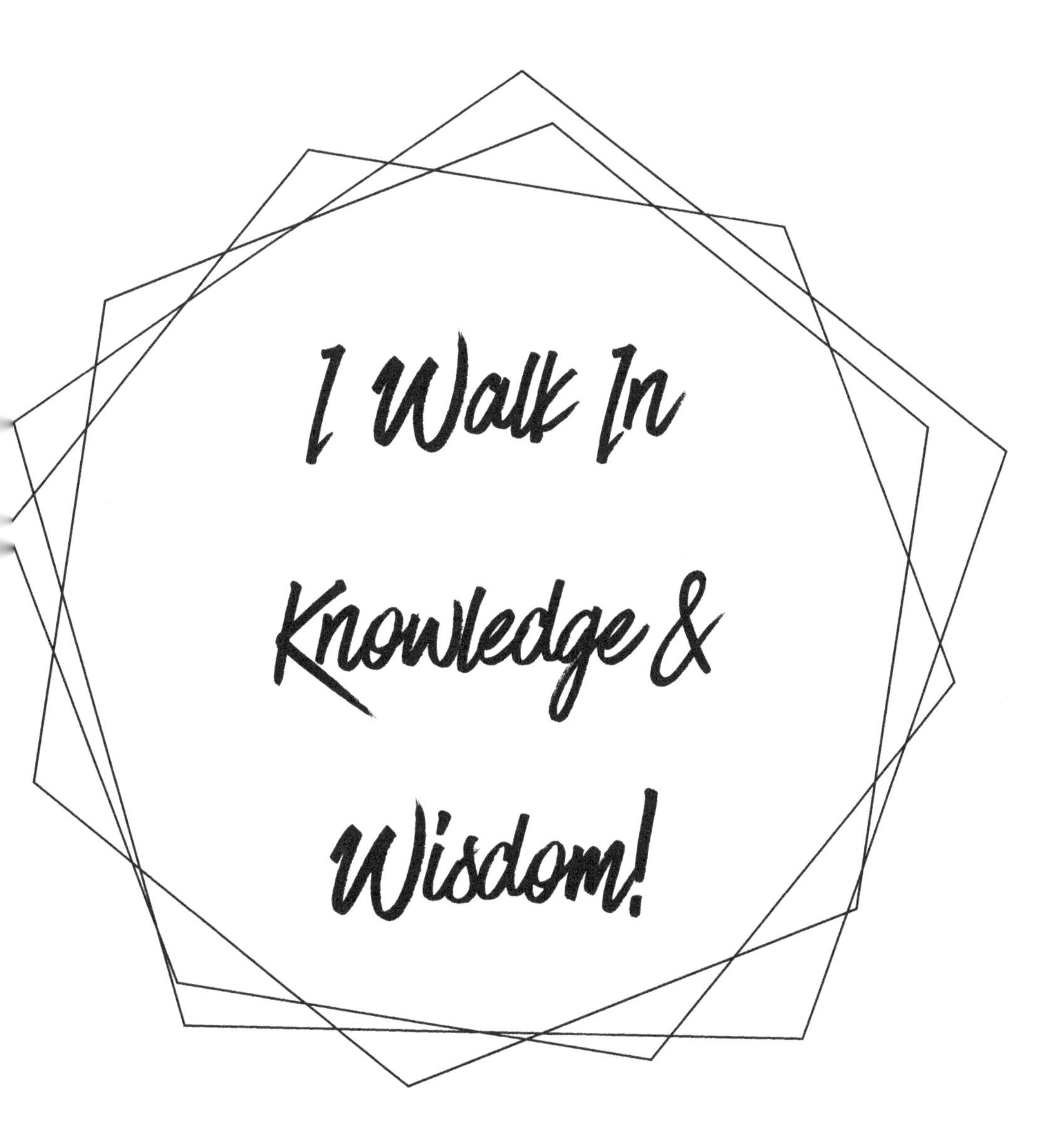
I Walk In
Knowledge &
Wisdom!

DATE

I've got this

M T W T F S S

TODAY I'M GRATEFUL FOR

TODAY'S TOP 3 GOALS/PRIORITIES

12 1 2 3 4 5 6 7 8 9 10 11

1.

2.

3.

MUST BE DONE TODAY

1.

2.

3.

APPOINTMENTS/TIME BLOCKS

TO DO LIST

- [ ]
- [ ]
- [ ]
- [ ]
- [ ]
- [ ]
- [ ]

HEALTH & FITNESS

MEAL PREP

NOTES

PERSONAL NOTES

DO TOMORROW

1.

2.

3.

WATER INTAKE

Day 19

DATE

M T W T F S S

ROMANS 7:25

I thank God through Jesus Christ our Lord. So then with the mind I myself serve the law of God; but with the flesh the law of sin.

How will you serve the law of God?

I Serve the
Lord With My
Whole Heart!

DATE

I've got this

M T W T F S S

TODAY I'M GRATEFUL FOR

TODAY'S TOP 3 GOALS/PRIORITIES

1.
2.
3.

12 1 2 3 4 5 6 7 8 9 10 11

MUST BE DONE TODAY

1.
2.
3.

APPOINTMENTS/TIME BLOCKS

TO DO LIST

- [ ]
- [ ]
- [ ]
- [ ]
- [ ]
- [ ]
- [ ]

HEALTH & FITNESS

MEAL PREP

NOTES

PERSONAL NOTES

DO TOMORROW

1.
2.
3.

WATER INTAKE

Day 20

DATE

M T W T F S S

PHILIPPIANS 4:8

Finally, brethren, whatsoever things are true, whatsoever things are honest, whatsoever things are just, whatsoever things are pure, whatsoever things are lovely, whatsoever things are of good report; if there be any virtue, and if there be any praise, think on these things.

What positive thinking moves you closer to God?

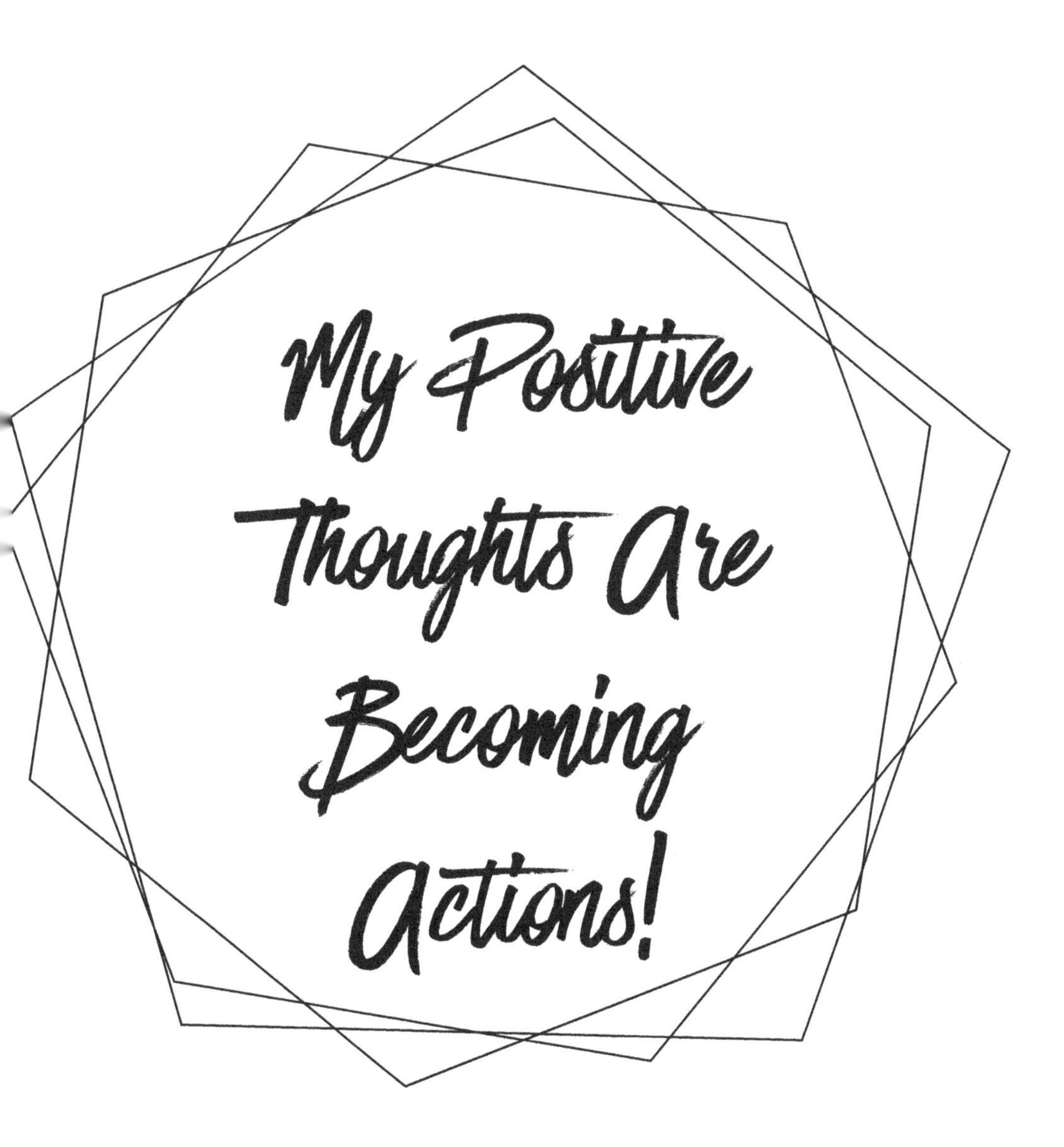
My Positive
Thoughts Are
Becoming
Actions!

DATE

I've got this

M T W T F S S

TODAY I'M GRATEFUL FOR

12 1 2 3 4 5 6 7 8 9 10 11

TODAY'S TOP 3 GOALS/PRIORITIES

1.

2.

3.

MUST BE DONE TODAY

1.

2.

3.

APPOINTMENTS/TIME BLOCKS

TO DO LIST

☐

☐

☐

☐

☐

☐

☐

HEALTH & FITNESS

MEAL PREP

NOTES

PERSONAL NOTES

WATER INTAKE

DO TOMORROW

1.

2.

3.

Day 21

DATE	

M T W T F S S

PHILIPPIANS 4:9

Those things, which ye have both learned, and received, and heard, and seen in me, do: and the God of peace shall be with you.

Do you apply what you hear and learn to your daily walk with God?

I Apply What
I Hear From
The Lord!

DATE

I've got this

M T W T F S S

TODAY I'M GRATEFUL FOR

12 1 2 3 4 5 6 7 8 9 10 11

TODAY'S TOP 3 GOALS/PRIORITIES

1.
2.
3.

MUST BE DONE TODAY

1.
2.
3.

APPOINTMENTS/TIME BLOCKS

TO DO LIST

- [ ]
- [ ]
- [ ]
- [ ]
- [ ]
- [ ]
- [ ]

HEALTH & FITNESS

MEAL PREP

NOTES

PERSONAL NOTES

DO TOMORROW

1.
2.
3.

WATER INTAKE

Day 22

DATE	

M T W T F S S

COLOSSIANS 3:2

Set your minds on things above, not on earthly things.

How will you set your mind on things above verses on earthly thing?

My Mind Is
Set On Things
Above!

DATE

I've got this

M T W T F S S

TODAY I'M GRATEFUL FOR

12 1 2 3 4 5 6 7 8 9 10 11

TODAY'S TOP 3 GOALS/PRIORITIES

1.

2.

3.

MUST BE DONE TODAY

1.

2.

3.

APPOINTMENTS/TIME BLOCKS

TO DO LIST

- [ ]
- [ ]
- [ ]
- [ ]
- [ ]
- [ ]
- [ ]

HEALTH & FITNESS

MEAL PREP

NOTES

PERSONAL NOTES

WATER INTAKE

DO TOMORROW

1.

2.

3.

Day 23

DATE	

M T W T F S S

2 CORINTHIANS 10:4

The weapons we fight with(A) are not the weapons of the world.
On the contrary, they have divine power(B) to demolish strongholds.(C)

How you use your spirituals weapons to reset your mind?

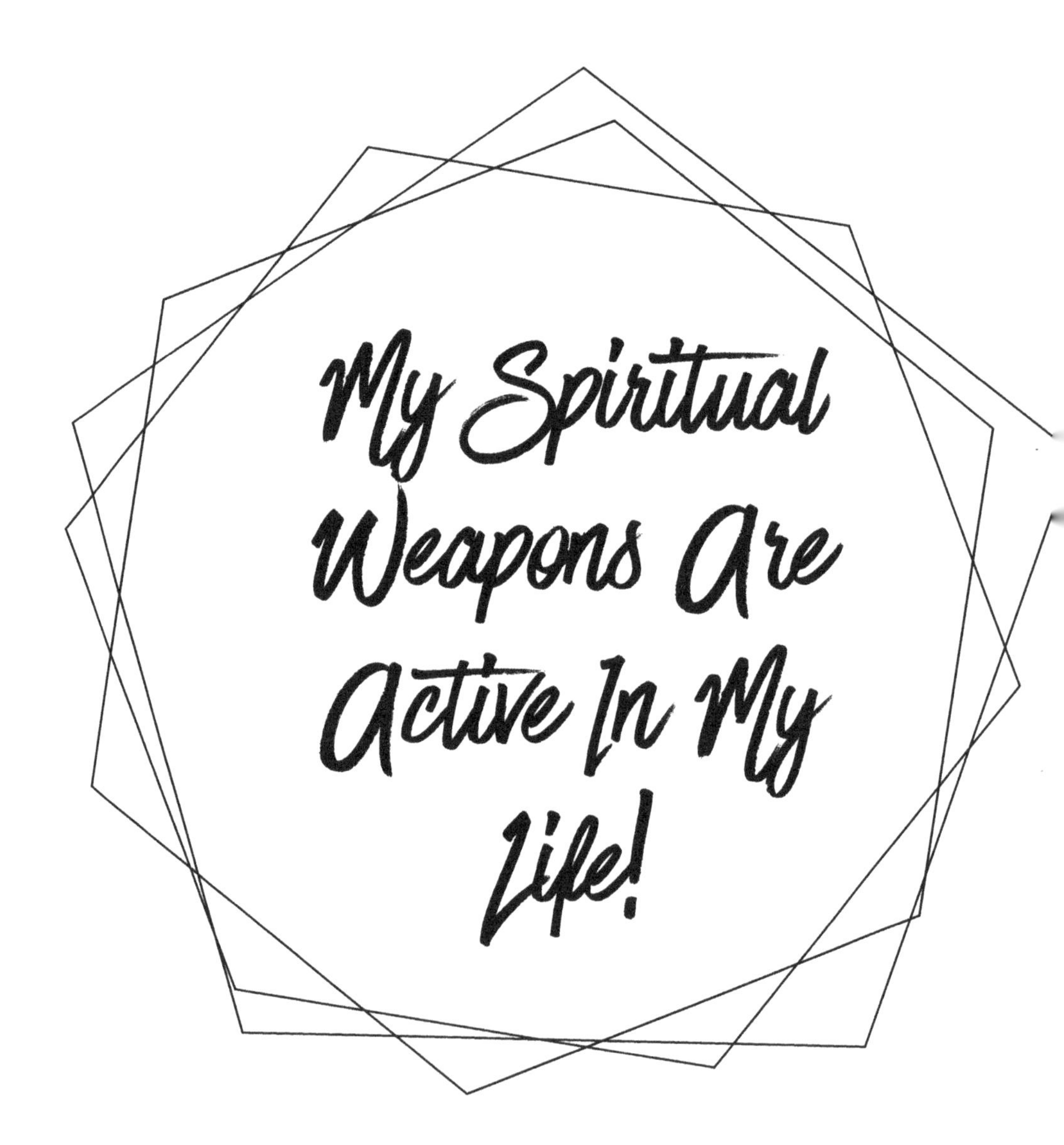
My Spiritual
Weapons Are
Active In My
Life!

DATE

I've got this

M T W T F S S

TODAY I'M GRATEFUL FOR

TODAY'S TOP 3 GOALS/PRIORITIES

12 1 2 3 4 5 6 7 8 9 10 11

1.

2.

3.

MUST BE DONE TODAY

1.

2.

3.

APPOINTMENTS/TIME BLOCKS

TO DO LIST

- ☐
- ☐
- ☐
- ☐
- ☐
- ☐
- ☐

HEALTH & FITNESS

MEAL PREP

NOTES

PERSONAL NOTES

DO TOMORROW

1.

2.

3.

WATER INTAKE

Day 24

DATE

M T W T F S S

JOHN 8:32

Then you will know the truth, and the truth will set you free.

How will you seek God to walk in total truth?

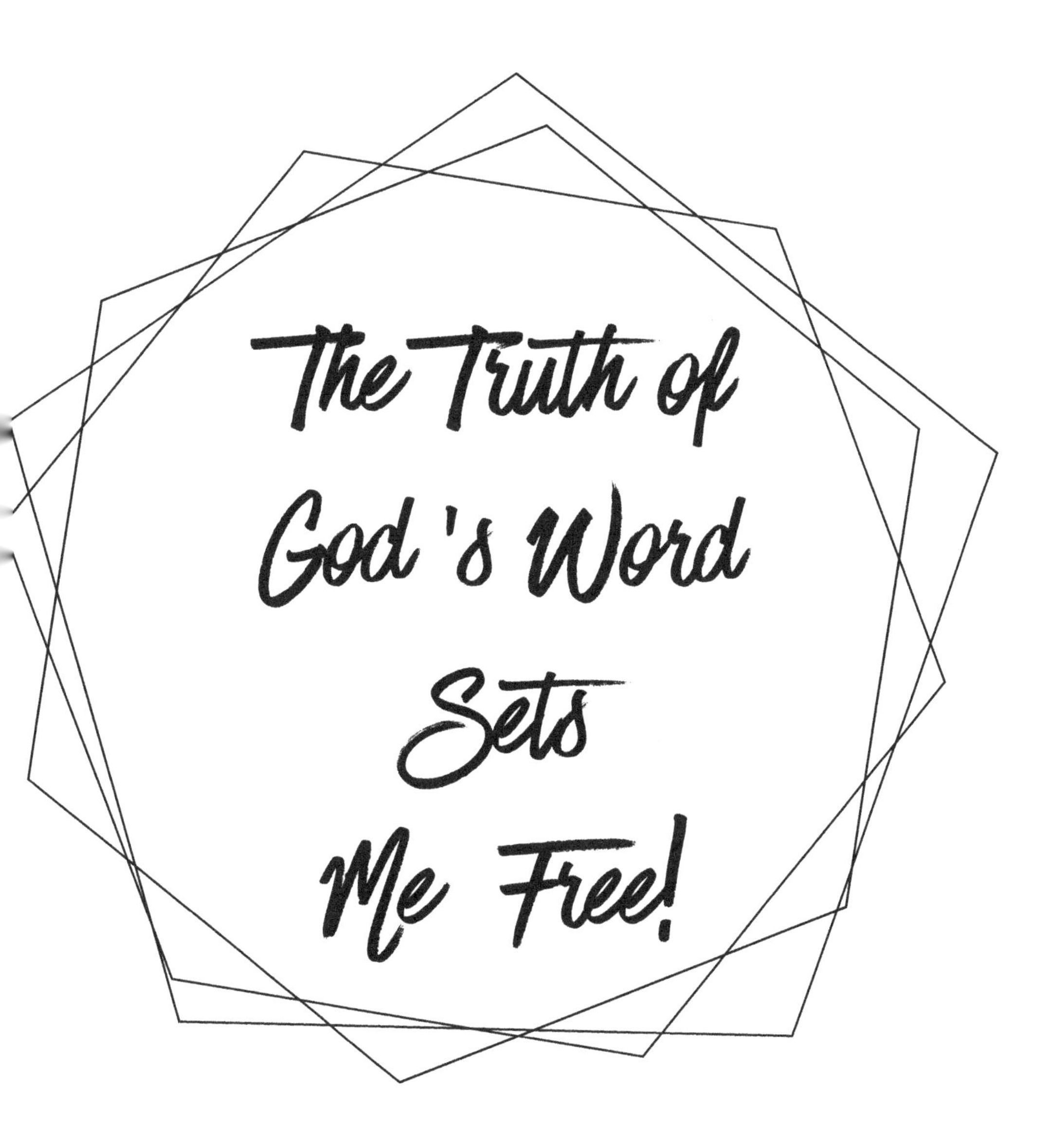
The Truth of
God's Word
Sets
Me Free!

DATE | I've got this | M T W T F S S

TODAY I'M GRATEFUL FOR

TODAY'S TOP 3 GOALS/PRIORITIES

12 1 2 3 4 5 6 7 8 9 10 11

1.

2.

3.

MUST BE DONE TODAY

1.

2.

3.

APPOINTMENTS/TIME BLOCKS

TO DO LIST

- [ ]
- [ ]
- [ ]
- [ ]
- [ ]
- [ ]
- [ ]

HEALTH & FITNESS

MEAL PREP

NOTES

PERSONAL NOTES

WATER INTAKE

DO TOMORROW

1.

2.

3.

Day 25

DATE

M T W T F S S

1 PETER 1:13

Therefore, with minds that are alert and fully sober,(set your hope(B) on the grace to be brought to you when Jesus Christ is revealed at his coming

How will you keep your mind on the coming of Christ Jesus?

My Mind Is
Fully Alert &
Sober!

DATE

I've got this

M T W T F S S

TODAY I'M GRATEFUL FOR

TODAY'S TOP 3 GOALS/PRIORITIES

1.

2.

3.

12 1 2 3 4 5 6 7 8 9 10 11

MUST BE DONE TODAY

1.

2.

3.

APPOINTMENTS/TIME BLOCKS

TO DO LIST

- [ ]
- [ ]
- [ ]
- [ ]
- [ ]
- [ ]
- [ ]

HEALTH & FITNESS

MEAL PREP

NOTES

PERSONAL NOTES

DO TOMORROW

1.

2.

3.

WATER INTAKE

Day 26

DATE	

M T W T F S S

MARK 8:33

But when Jesus turned and looked at his disciples, he rebuked Peter. "Get behind me, Satan!"(A) he said. "You do not have in mind the concerns of God, but merely human concerns."

Are you concerned about the things of God?

I Have
The Mind of
God!

DATE

I've got this

M T W T F S S

TODAY I'M GRATEFUL FOR

12 1 2 3 4 5 6 7 8 9 10 11

TODAY'S TOP 3 GOALS/PRIORITIES

1.

2.

3.

MUST BE DONE TODAY

1.

2.

3.

APPOINTMENTS/TIME BLOCKS

TO DO LIST

- [ ]
- [ ]
- [ ]
- [ ]
- [ ]
- [ ]
- [ ]

HEALTH & FITNESS

MEAL PREP

NOTES

PERSONAL NOTES

WATER INTAKE

DO TOMORROW

1.

2.

3.

Day 27

DATE	

M T W T F S S

LUKE 24:45

Then he opened their minds so they could understand the Scriptures.

Do you inquire the Lord for understanding?

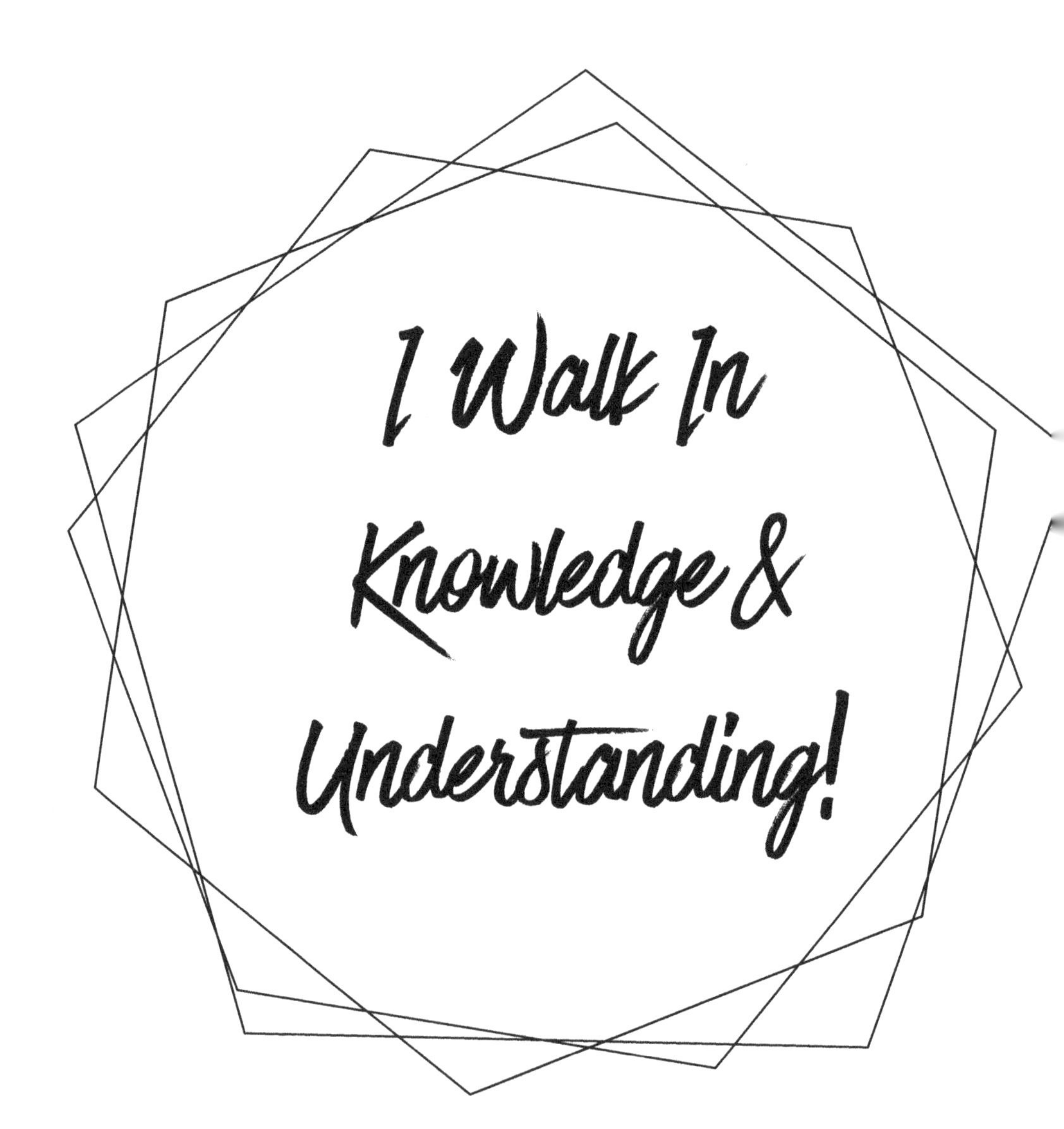
I Walk In
Knowledge &
Understanding!

DATE

I've got this

M T W T F S S

TODAY I'M GRATEFUL FOR

12 1 2 3 4 5 6 7 8 9 10 11

TODAY'S TOP 3 GOALS/PRIORITIES

1.

2.

3.

MUST BE DONE TODAY

1.

2.

3.

APPOINTMENTS/TIME BLOCKS

TO DO LIST

- [ ]
- [ ]
- [ ]
- [ ]
- [ ]
- [ ]
- [ ]

HEALTH & FITNESS

MEAL PREP

NOTES

PERSONAL NOTES

DO TOMORROW

1.

2.

3.

WATER INTAKE

Day 28

DATE	

M T W T F S S

PHILIPPIANS 2:5

In your relationships with one another, have the same mindset as Christ Jesus:(A)

How will you encourage your brothers and sisters in Christ?

I Encourage
My Brothers &
Sisters In
Christ!

DATE

I've got this

M T W T F S S

TODAY I'M GRATEFUL FOR

12 1 2 3 4 5 6 7 8 9 10 11

TODAY'S TOP 3 GOALS/PRIORITIES

1.
2.
3.

MUST BE DONE TODAY

1.
2.
3.

APPOINTMENTS/TIME BLOCKS

TO DO LIST

- ☐
- ☐
- ☐
- ☐
- ☐
- ☐
- ☐

HEALTH & FITNESS

MEAL PREP

NOTES

PERSONAL NOTES

WATER INTAKE

DO TOMORROW

1.
2.
3.

Day 29

DATE	

M T W T F S S

1 CORINTHIANS2:16

for, "Who has known the mind of the Lord so as to instruct him?"

How will you seek God to understand His power?

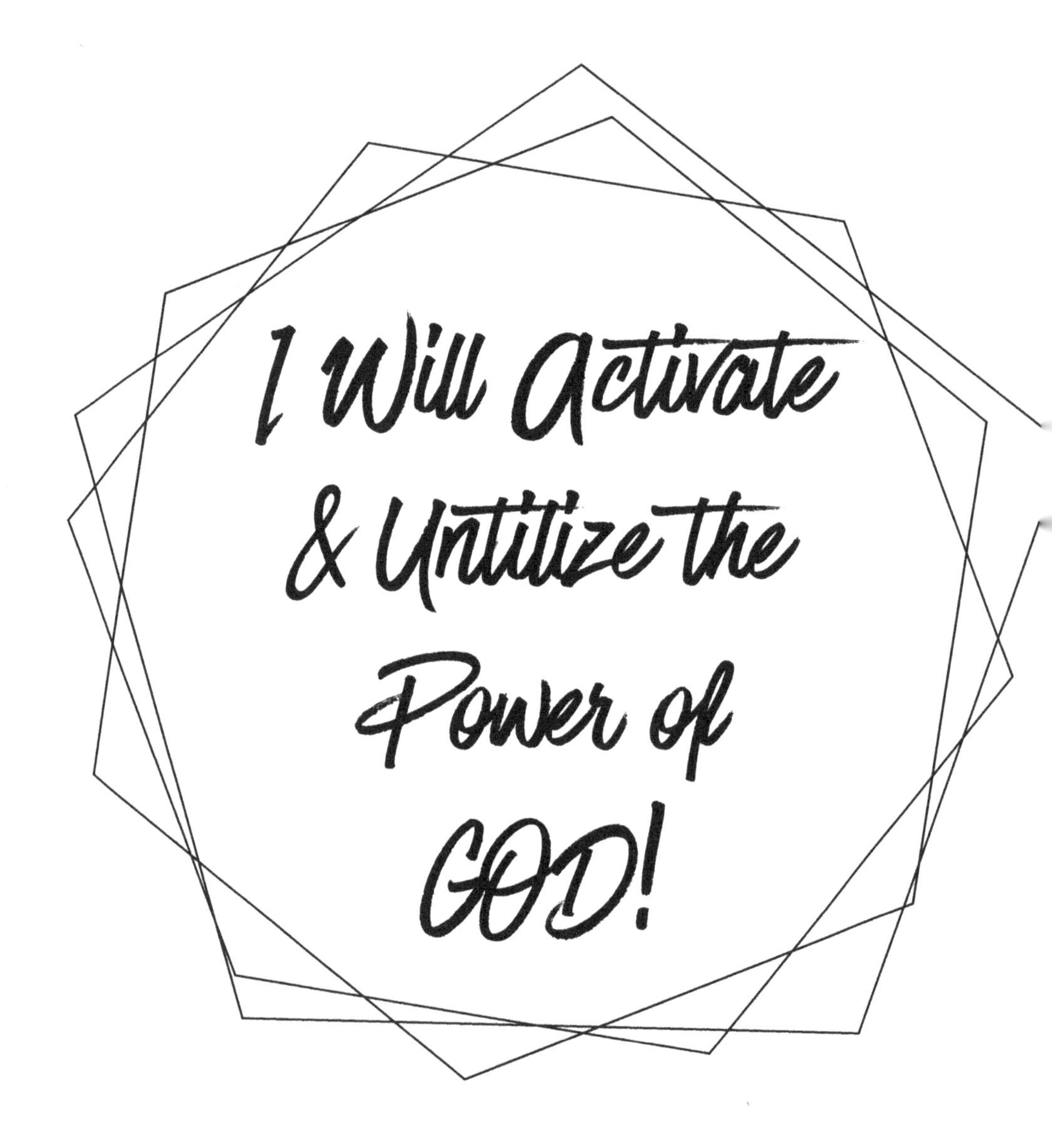
I Will Activate
& Untilize the
Power of
GOD!

DATE

I've got this

M T W T F S S

TODAY I'M GRATEFUL FOR

12 11 1 10 2 9 3 8 4 7 5 6

TODAY'S TOP 3 GOALS/PRIORITIES

1.

2.

3.

MUST BE DONE TODAY

1.

2.

3.

APPOINTMENTS/TIME BLOCKS

TO DO LIST

- ☐
- ☐
- ☐
- ☐
- ☐
- ☐
- ☐

HEALTH & FITNESS

MEAL PREP

NOTES

PERSONAL NOTES

WATER INTAKE

DO TOMORROW

1.

2.

3.

Day 30

DATE

M T W T F S S

PHILIPPIANS 2:2

then make my joy complete(A) by being like-minded,(B) having the same love, being one(C) in spirit and of one mind.

How will you stay on one accord with the Holy Spirit?

My Joy
Is Complete!

DATE

I've got this

M T W T F S S

TODAY I'M GRATEFUL FOR

12 1 2 3 4 5 6 7 8 9 10 11

TODAY'S TOP 3 GOALS/PRIORITIES

1.

2.

3.

MUST BE DONE TODAY

1.

2.

3.

APPOINTMENTS/TIME BLOCKS

TO DO LIST

- [ ]
- [ ]
- [ ]
- [ ]
- [ ]
- [ ]
- [ ]

HEALTH & FITNESS

MEAL PREP

NOTES

PERSONAL NOTES

WATER INTAKE

DO TOMORROW

1.

2.

3.

MONTHLY GOALS

MONDAY	TUESDAY	WEDNESDAY

NOTES

THURSDAY	FRIDAY	SATURDAY	SUNDAY

MONTHLY GOALS

MONDAY	TUESDAY	WEDNESDAY

NOTES

THURSDAY	FRIDAY	SATURDAY	SUNDAY

MONTHLY GOALS

MONDAY	TUESDAY	WEDNESDAY

NOTES

THURSDAY	FRIDAY	SATURDAY	SUNDAY

MONTHLY GOALS	MONDAY	TUESDAY	WEDNESDAY

NOTES

THURSDAY	FRIDAY	SATURDAY	SUNDAY

MONTHLY GOALS

MONDAY	TUESDAY	WEDNESDAY

NOTES

THURSDAY	FRIDAY	SATURDAY	SUNDAY

MONTHLY GOALS

MONDAY	TUESDAY	WEDNESDAY

NOTES

THURSDAY	FRIDAY	SATURDAY	SUNDAY

MONTHLY GOALS

MONDAY	TUESDAY	WEDNESDAY

NOTES

THURSDAY	FRIDAY	SATURDAY	SUNDAY

MONTHLY GOALS

MONDAY	TUESDAY	WEDNESDAY

NOTES

THURSDAY	FRIDAY	SATURDAY	SUNDAY

MONTHLY GOALS

MONDAY	TUESDAY	WEDNESDAY

NOTES

THURSDAY	FRIDAY	SATURDAY	SUNDAY

MONTHLY GOALS

MONDAY	TUESDAY	WEDNESDAY

NOTES

THURSDAY	FRIDAY	SATURDAY	SUNDAY

MONTHLY GOALS

MONDAY	TUESDAY	WEDNESDAY

NOTES

THURSDAY	FRIDAY	SATURDAY	SUNDAY

MONTHLY GOALS	MONDAY	TUESDAY	WEDNESDAY

NOTES

THURSDAY	FRIDAY	SATURDAY	SUNDAY

Made in the USA
Monee, IL
17 January 2021